W9-BXG-332

Table of Contents

Student Name: _____   Notebook Number:_____

Email: _____   Phone: _____

Network ID: _____   Course:_____

Lab Instructor: _____   Section: _____   Semester: _____

Lab Partners:_____

Date	Experiment/Subject	Page Number

THE HAYDEN-McNEIL STUDENT LAB NOTEBOOK

Table of Contents

Date	Experiment/Subject	Page Number

THE HAYDEN-McNEIL STUDENT LAB NOTEBOOK

Exp. No.	Experiment/Subject		Date	
Name	Lab Partner		Locker/ Desk No.	Course & Section No.

Signature	Date	Witness/TA	Date

Exp. No.	Experiment/Subject		Date	
Name	Lab Partner		Locker/Desk No.	Course & Section No.

Signature		Date	Witness/TA		Date

THE HAYDEN-McNEIL STUDENT LAB NOTEBOOK

Note: Place fold-over back cover under copy sheet before writing

Exp. No.	Experiment/Subject		Date	
Name	Lab Partner		Locker/ Desk No.	Course & Section No.

COPY

Signature		Date	Witness/TA	Date

Note: Place fold-over back cover under copy sheet before writing

Exp. No.	Experiment/Subject		Date	
Name		Lab Partner	Locker/ Desk No.	Course & Section No.

Exp. No.	Experiment/Subject		Date	
Name	Lab Partner		Locker/ Desk No.	Course & Section No.

Signature	Date	Witness/TA	Date

THE HAYDEN-McNEIL STUDENT LAB NOTEBOOK

Note: Place fold-over back cover under copy sheet before writing

Exp. No.	Experiment/Subject		Date	
Name		Lab Partner	Locker/ Desk No.	Course & Section No.

Signature		Date	Witness/TA		Date

Exp. No.	Experiment/Subject		Date	
Name		Lab Partner	Locker/ Desk No.	Course & Section No.

Signature		Date	Witness/TA		Date

Exp. No.	Experiment/Subject		Date	
Name	Lab Partner		Locker/ Desk No.	Course & Section No.

Signature		Date	Witness/TA		Date

Exp. No.	Experiment/Subject		Date	
Name	Lab Partner		Locker/ Desk No.	Course & Section No.

Exp. No.	Experiment/Subject		Date	
Name	Lab Partner		Locker/ Desk No.	Course & Section No.

Signature		Date	Witness/TA	Date

Exp. No.	Experiment/Subject		Date	
Name	Lab Partner		Locker/ Desk No.	Course & Section No.

Signature		Date	Witness/TA		Date

Exp. No.	Experiment/Subject		Date	
Name		Lab Partner	Locker/ Desk No.	Course & Section No.

Signature		Date	Witness/TA		Date

Exp. No.	Experiment/Subject		Date	
Name		Lab Partner	Locker/ Desk No.	Course & Section No.

Signature		Date	Witness/TA		Date

Exp. No.	Experiment/Subject		Date	
Name		Lab Partner	Locker/ Desk No.	Course & Section No.

Signature		Date	Witness/TA		Date

Exp. No.	Experiment/Subject		Date	
Name	Lab Partner		Locker/ Desk No.	Course & Section No.

Signature	Date	Witness/TA		Date

Exp. No.	Experiment/Subject		Date	
Name		Lab Partner	Locker/ Desk No.	Course & Section No.

Signature	Date	Witness/TA	Date

THE HAYDEN-McNEIL STUDENT LAB NOTEBOOK   Note: Place fold-over back cover under copy sheet before writing

Exp. No.	Experiment/Subject		Date	
Name		Lab Partner	Locker/ Desk No.	Course & Section No.

Signature		Date	Witness/TA		Date

Exp. No.	Experiment/Subject		Date	
Name		Lab Partner	Locker/ Desk No.	Course & Section No.

Signature		Date	Witness/TA		Date

THE HAYDEN-McNEIL STUDENT LAB NOTEBOOK   Note: Place fold-over back cover under copy sheet before writing

Exp. No.	Experiment/Subject		Date	
Name	Lab Partner		Locker/ Desk No.	Course & Section No.

Signature	Date	Witness/TA	Date

Exp. No.	Experiment/Subject		Date	
Name		Lab Partner	Locker/ Desk No.	Course & Section No.

Signature		Date	Witness/TA		Date

THE HAYDEN-McNEIL STUDENT LAB NOTEBOOK   Note: Place fold-over back cover under copy sheet before writing

Exp. No.	Experiment/Subject		Date	
Name	Lab Partner		Locker/ Desk No.	Course & Section No.

Signature	Date	Witness/TA		Date

THE HAYDEN-McNEIL STUDENT LAB NOTEBOOK   Note: Place fold-over back cover under copy sheet before writing

Exp. No.	Experiment/Subject		Date	
Name		Lab Partner	Locker/ Desk No.	Course & Section No.

Signature		Date	Witness/TA		Date

Exp. No.	Experiment/Subject		Date	
Name		Lab Partner	Locker/ Desk No.	Course & Section No.

Signature		Date	Witness/TA		Date

Exp. No.	Experiment/Subject		Date	
Name	Lab Partner		Locker/ Desk No.	Course & Section No.

Signature	Date	Witness/TA	Date

Exp. No.	Experiment/Subject		Date	
Name	Lab Partner		Locker/ Desk No.	Course & Section No.

Signature		Date	Witness/TA	Date

Exp. No.	Experiment/Subject		Date	
Name	Lab Partner		Locker/ Desk No.	Course & Section No.

Signature		Date	Witness/TA	Date

Exp. No.	Experiment/Subject		Date	
Name	Lab Partner		Locker/ Desk No.	Course & Section No.

Signature		Date	Witness/TA		Date

Exp. No.	Experiment/Subject		Date	
Name	Lab Partner		Locker/ Desk No.	Course & Section No.

Note: Place fold-over back cover under copy sheet before writing

Signature	Date	Witness/TA	Date

Exp. No.	Experiment/Subject		Date	
Name	Lab Partner		Locker/ Desk No.	Course & Section No.

COPY

Signature	Date	Witness/TA		Date

Exp. No.	Experiment/Subject		Date	
Name	Lab Partner		Locker/ Desk No.	Course & Section No.

Signature		Date	Witness/TA		Date

Exp. No.	Experiment/Subject		Date	
Name	Lab Partner		Locker/ Desk No.	Course & Section No.

Signature		Date	Witness/TA		Date

Exp. No.	Experiment/Subject		Date	
Name	Lab Partner		Locker/ Desk No.	Course & Section No.

Signature	Date	Witness/TA		Date

Exp. No.	Experiment/Subject		Date	
Name	Lab Partner		Locker/ Desk No.	Course & Section No.

Exp. No.	Experiment/Subject		Date	
Name	Lab Partner		Locker/ Desk No.	Course & Section No.

COPY

Signature		Date	Witness/TA	Date

Exp. No.	Experiment/Subject		Date	
Name	Lab Partner		Locker/ Desk No.	Course & Section No.

Exp. No.	Experiment/Subject		Date	
Name	Lab Partner		Locker/ Desk No.	Course & Section No.

Signature		Date	Witness/TA	Date

Exp. No.	Experiment/Subject		Date	
Name	Lab Partner		Locker/ Desk No.	Course & Section No.

Signature	Date	Witness/TA	Date

Exp. No.	Experiment/Subject		Date	
Name	Lab Partner		Locker/ Desk No.	Course & Section No.

Signature		Date	Witness/TA		Date

Exp. No.	Experiment/Subject		Date	
Name	Lab Partner		Locker/ Desk No.	Course & Section No.

Signature	Date	Witness/TA		Date

THE HAYDEN-McNEIL STUDENT LAB NOTEBOOK   Note: Place fold-over back cover under copy sheet before writing

Exp. No.	Experiment/Subject		Date	
Name	Lab Partner		Locker/ Desk No.	Course & Section No.

Signature	Date	Witness/TA		Date

THE HAYDEN-McNEIL STUDENT LAB NOTEBOOK   Note: Place fold-over back cover under copy sheet before writing

Exp. No.	Experiment/Subject		Date	
Name	Lab Partner		Locker/ Desk No.	Course & Section No.

Signature		Date	Witness/TA		Date

THE HAYDEN-McNEIL STUDENT LAB NOTEBOOK

Note: Place fold-over back cover under copy sheet before writing

Exp. No.	Experiment/Subject		Date	
Name		Lab Partner	Locker/ Desk No.	Course & Section No.

Signature		Date	Witness/TA		Date

Exp. No.	Experiment/Subject		Date	
Name	Lab Partner		Locker/ Desk No.	Course & Section No.

Signature		Date	Witness/TA		Date

THE HAYDEN-McNEIL STUDENT LAB NOTEBOOK   Note: Place fold-over back cover under copy sheet before writing

Exp. No.	Experiment/Subject		Date	
Name		Lab Partner	Locker/ Desk No.	Course & Section No.

Signature		Date	Witness/TA		Date

Exp. No.	Experiment/Subject		Date	
Name	Lab Partner		Locker/ Desk No.	Course & Section No.

Signature		Date	Witness/TA		Date

Exp. No.	Experiment/Subject		Date	
Name	Lab Partner		Locker/ Desk No.	Course & Section No.

Signature	Date	Witness/TA	Date

Note: Place fold-over back cover under copy sheet before writing

Exp. No.	Experiment/Subject		Date	
Name	Lab Partner		Locker/ Desk No.	Course & Section No.

COPY

Signature		Date	Witness/TA		Date

Note: Please fold over back cover or under copy sheet before writing

Exp. No.	Experiment/Subject		Date	
Name	Lab Partner		Locker/ Desk No.	Course & Section No.

Signature	Date	Witness/TA	Date

THE HAYDEN-McNEIL STUDENT LAB NOTEBOOK   Note: Place fold-over back cover under copy sheet before writing

Exp. No.	Experiment/Subject		Date	
Name		Lab Partner	Locker/ Desk No.	Course & Section No.

Signature		Date	Witness/TA		Date

Exp. No.	Experiment/Subject		Date	
Name	Lab Partner		Locker/ Desk No.	Course & Section No.

Signature		Date	Witness/TA		Date

Exp. No.	Experiment/Subject		Date	
Name	Lab Partner		Locker/ Desk No.	Course & Section No.

Signature		Date	Witness/TA		Date

Exp. No.	Experiment/Subject		Date	
Name	Lab Partner		Locker/ Desk No.	Course & Section No.

Signature		Date	Witness/TA		Date

THE HAYDEN-McNEIL STUDENT LAB NOTEBOOK

Note: Place fold-over back cover under copy sheet before writing

Exp. No.	Experiment/Subject		Date	
Name	Lab Partner		Locker/ Desk No.	Course & Section No.

COPY

Signature		Date	Witness/TA	Date

Exp. No.	Experiment/Subject		Date	
Name	Lab Partner		Locker/ Desk No.	Course & Section No.

Signature		Date	Witness/TA		Date

Exp. No.	Experiment/Subject		Date	
Name	Lab Partner		Locker/ Desk No.	Course & Section No.

Signature		Date	Witness/TA		Date

Exp. No.	Experiment/Subject		Date	
Name	Lab Partner		Locker/ Desk No.	Course & Section No.

Signature		Date	Witness/TA		Date

THE HAYDEN-McNEIL STUDENT LAB NOTEBOOK

Note: Place fold-over back cover under copy sheet before writing

Exp. No.	Experiment/Subject		Date	
Name	Lab Partner		Locker/ Desk No.	Course & Section No.

COPY

Signature		Date	Witness/TA		Date

Exp. No.	Experiment/Subject		Date	
Name	Lab Partner		Locker/ Desk No.	Course & Section No.

Signature		Date	Witness/TA		Date

Exp. No.	Experiment/Subject		Date	
Name	Lab Partner		Locker/ Desk No.	Course & Section No.

Signature		Date	Witness/TA		Date

Exp. No.	Experiment/Subject		Date	
Name	Lab Partner		Locker/ Desk No.	Course & Section No.

Signature	Date	Witness/TA	Date

Exp. No.	Experiment/Subject		Date	
Name	Lab Partner		Locker/ Desk No.	Course & Section No.

Exp. No.	Experiment/Subject		Date	
Name	Lab Partner		Locker/ Desk No.	Course & Section No.

Signature		Date	Witness/TA		Date

Exp. No.	Experiment/Subject		Date	
Name	Lab Partner		Locker/ Desk No.	Course & Section No.

Signature		Date	Witness/TA		Date

Exp. No.	Experiment/Subject		Date	
Name	Lab Partner		Locker/ Desk No.	Course & Section No.

Signature		Date	Witness/TA		Date

Exp. No.	Experiment/Subject		Date	
Name	Lab Partner		Locker/ Desk No.	Course & Section No.

Signature	Date	Witness/TA	Date

Note: Place fold-over back cover under copy sheet before writing

Exp. No.	Experiment/Subject		Date	
Name	Lab Partner		Locker/ Desk No.	Course & Section No.

Signature	Date	Witness/TA	Date

Exp. No.	Experiment/Subject		Date	
Name	Lab Partner		Locker/ Desk No.	Course & Section No.

Signature	Date	Witness/TA	Date

Note: Place fold-over back cover under copy sheet before writing

Exp. No.	Experiment/Subject		Date	
Name	Lab Partner		Locker/ Desk No.	Course & Section No.

Signature	Date	Witness/TA	Date

THE HAYDEN-McNEIL STUDENT LAB NOTEBOOK

Note: Place fold-over back cover under copy sheet before writing

Exp. No.	Experiment/Subject		Date	
Name	Lab Partner		Locker/ Desk No.	Course & Section No.

Signature	Date	Witness/TA	Date

Note: Place fold-over back cover under copy sheet before writing

Exp. No.	Experiment/Subject		Date	
Name		Lab Partner	Locker/ Desk No.	Course & Section No.

COPY

Signature		Date	Witness/TA		Date

Exp. No.	Experiment/Subject		Date	
Name	Lab Partner		Locker/ Desk No.	Course & Section No.

Signature	Date	Witness/TA	Date

Note: Place fold-over back cover under copy sheet before writing

Exp. No.	Experiment/Subject		Date	
Name	Lab Partner		Locker/ Desk No.	Course & Section No.

Signature		Date	Witness/TA		Date

Exp. No.	Experiment/Subject		Date	
Name	Lab Partner		Locker/ Desk No.	Course & Section No.

COPY

Exp. No.	Experiment/Subject		Date	
Name	Lab Partner		Locker/ Desk No.	Course & Section No.

Signature		Date	Witness/TA		Date

THE HAYDEN-McNEIL STUDENT LAB NOTEBOOK

Note: Place fold-over back cover under copy sheet before writing

Exp. No.	Experiment/Subject		Date	
Name		Lab Partner	Locker/ Desk No.	Course & Section No.

Signature		Date	Witness/TA		Date

THE HAYDEN-McNEIL STUDENT LAB NOTEBOOK

Note: Place fold-over back cover under copy sheet before writing

Exp. No.	Experiment/Subject		Date	
Name	Lab Partner		Locker/ Desk No.	Course & Section No.

Signature	Date	Witness/TA	Date

THE HAYDEN-McNEIL STUDENT LAB NOTEBOOK   Note: Place fold-over back cover under copy sheet before writing

Exp. No.	Experiment/Subject		Date	
Name	Lab Partner		Locker/ Desk No.	Course & Section No.

Signature	Date	Witness/TA	Date

Exp. No.	Experiment/Subject		Date	
Name		Lab Partner	Locker/ Desk No.	Course & Section No.

Signature	Date	Witness/TA	Date

Exp. No.	Experiment/Subject		Date	
Name	Lab Partner		Locker/ Desk No.	Course & Section No.

Signature	Date	Witness/TA	Date

Exp. No.	Experiment/Subject		Date	
Name	Lab Partner		Locker/ Desk No.	Course & Section No.

Signature	Date	Witness/TA		Date

Exp. No.	Experiment/Subject		Date	
Name	Lab Partner		Locker/ Desk No.	Course & Section No.

Signature		Date	Witness/TA		Date

Exp. No.	Experiment/Subject		Date	
Name	Lab Partner		Locker/ Desk No.	Course & Section No.

Signature	Date	Witness/TA	Date

THE HAYDEN-McNEIL STUDENT LAB NOTEBOOK   Note: Place fold-over back cover under copy sheet before writing

Exp. No.	Experiment/Subject		Date	
Name	Lab Partner		Locker/ Desk No.	Course & Section No.

Signature	Date	Witness/TA	Date

Exp. No.	Experiment/Subject		Date	
Name	Lab Partner		Locker/ Desk No.	Course & Section No.

Signature		Date	Witness/TA		Date

Exp. No.	Experiment/Subject		Date	
Name	Lab Partner		Locker/ Desk No.	Course & Section No.

Signature	Date	Witness/TA	Date

THE HAYDEN-McNEIL STUDENT LAB NOTEBOOK

Note: Place fold-over back cover under copy sheet before writing

Exp. No.	Experiment/Subject		Date	
Name		Lab Partner	Locker/ Desk No.	Course & Section No.

Exp. No.	Experiment/Subject		Date	
Name	Lab Partner		Locker/ Desk No.	Course & Section No.

Signature	Date	Witness/TA	Date

Note: Place fold-over back cover under copy sheet before writing

Exp. No.	Experiment/Subject		Date	
Name		Lab Partner	Locker/ Desk No.	Course & Section No.

Signature	Date	Witness/TA	Date

Exp. No.	Experiment/Subject		Date	
Name		Lab Partner	Locker/ Desk No.	Course & Section No.

Signature		Date	Witness/TA		Date

Exp. No.	Experiment/Subject		Date	
Name		Lab Partner	Locker/ Desk No.	Course & Section No.

Signature		Date	Witness/TA		Date

THE HAYDEN-McNEIL STUDENT LAB NOTEBOOK

Note: Place fold-over back cover under copy sheet before writing

Exp. No.	Experiment/Subject		Date	
Name	Lab Partner		Locker/ Desk No.	Course & Section No.

Signature		Date	Witness/TA		Date

Exp. No.	Experiment/Subject		Date	
Name		Lab Partner	Locker/ Desk No.	Course & Section No.

Signature		Date	Witness/TA		Date

Exp. No.	Experiment/Subject		Date	
Name	Lab Partner		Locker/ Desk No.	Course & Section No.

Signature		Date	Witness/TA		Date

Exp. No.	Experiment/Subject		Date	
Name	Lab Partner		Locker/ Desk No.	Course & Section No.

Signature	Date	Witness/TA	Date

Note: Place fold-over back cover under copy sheet before writing

Exp. No.	Experiment/Subject		Date	
Name	Lab Partner		Locker/ Desk No.	Course & Section No.

Signature		Date	Witness/TA		Date

THE HAYDEN-McNEIL STUDENT LAB NOTEBOOK   Note: Place fold-over back cover under copy sheet before writing

Exp. No.	Experiment/Subject		Date	
Name		Lab Partner	Locker/ Desk No.	Course & Section No.

Signature		Date	Witness/TA		Date

Exp. No.	Experiment/Subject		Date	
Name	Lab Partner		Locker/ Desk No.	Course & Section No.

Signature	Date	Witness/TA	Date

Exp. No.	Experiment/Subject		Date	
Name	Lab Partner		Locker/ Desk No.	Course & Section No.

Signature		Date	Witness/TA		Date

Exp. No.	Experiment/Subject		Date	
Name	Lab Partner		Locker/ Desk No.	Course & Section No.

Signature		Date	Witness/TA		Date

Exp. No.	Experiment/Subject		Date	
Name		Lab Partner	Locker/ Desk No.	Course & Section No.

Signature		Date	Witness/TA		Date

Exp. No.	Experiment/Subject		Date	
Name		Lab Partner	Locker/ Desk No.	Course & Section No.

Signature		Date	Witness/TA		Date

Exp. No.	Experiment/Subject		Date	
Name	Lab Partner		Locker/ Desk No.	Course & Section No.

Signature		Date	Witness/TA		Date

Exp. No.	Experiment/Subject		Date	
Name		Lab Partner	Locker/ Desk No.	Course & Section No.

Signature		Date	Witness/TA		Date

Exp. No.	Experiment/Subject		Date	
Name		Lab Partner	Locker/ Desk No.	Course & Section No.

Signature		Date	Witness/TA		Date

Exp. No.	Experiment/Subject		Date	
Name	Lab Partner		Locker/ Desk No.	Course & Section No.

COPY

Signature		Date	Witness/TA		Date

THE HAYDEN-McNEIL STUDENT LAB NOTEBOOK   Note: Place fold-over back cover under copy sheet before writing

Exp. No.	Experiment/Subject		Date	
Name	Lab Partner		Locker/ Desk No.	Course & Section No.

Signature		Date	Witness/TA		Date

Exp. No.	Experiment/Subject		Date	
Name		Lab Partner	Locker/ Desk No.	Course & Section No.

COPY

Signature		Date	Witness/TA		Date

THE HAYDEN-McNEIL STUDENT LAB NOTEBOOK   Note: Place fold-over back cover under copy sheet before writing

Exp. No.	Experiment/Subject		Date	
Name	Lab Partner		Locker/ Desk No.	Course & Section No.

Signature		Date	Witness/TA		Date

Exp. No.	Experiment/Subject		Date	
Name	Lab Partner		Locker/ Desk No.	Course & Section No.

Signature		Date	Witness/TA		Date

Exp. No.	Experiment/Subject		Date	
Name	Lab Partner		Locker/ Desk No.	Course & Section No.

COPY

Signature	Date	Witness/TA		Date

THE HAYDEN-McNEIL STUDENT LAB NOTEBOOK   Note: Place fold-over back cover under copy sheet before writing

Exp. No.	Experiment/Subject		Date	
Name	Lab Partner		Locker/ Desk No.	Course & Section No.

Signature	Date	Witness/TA		Date

Exp. No.	Experiment/Subject		Date	
Name		Lab Partner	Locker/ Desk No.	Course & Section No.

Signature		Date	Witness/TA	Date

Exp. No.	Experiment/Subject		Date	
Name		Lab Partner	Locker/ Desk No.	Course & Section No.

Signature		Date	Witness/TA		Date

Exp. No.	Experiment/Subject		Date	
Name		Lab Partner	Locker/ Desk No.	Course & Section No.

Signature		Date	Witness/TA		Date

Exp. No.	Experiment/Subject		Date	
Name	Lab Partner		Locker/ Desk No.	Course & Section No.

COPY

Signature	Date	Witness/TA		Date

Exp. No.	Experiment/Subject		Date	
Name		Lab Partner	Locker/ Desk No.	Course & Section No.

Signature		Date	Witness/TA		Date

Note: Place fold-over back cover under copy sheet before writing

Exp. No.	Experiment/Subject		Date	
Name	Lab Partner		Locker/ Desk No.	Course & Section No.

COPY

Signature	Date	Witness/TA	Date

Note: Place fold-over back cover under copy sheet before writing

Exp. No.	Experiment/Subject		Date	
Name		Lab Partner	Locker/ Desk No.	Course & Section No.

Signature		Date	Witness/TA		Date

THE HAYDEN-McNEIL STUDENT LAB NOTEBOOK

Note: Place fold-over back cover under copy sheet before writing

Exp. No.	Experiment/Subject		Date	
Name	Lab Partner		Locker/ Desk No.	Course & Section No.

Signature		Date	Witness/TA		Date

THE HAYDEN-McNEIL STUDENT LAB NOTEBOOK

Note: Place fold-over back cover under copy sheet before writing

Exp. No.	Experiment/Subject		Date	
Name	Lab Partner		Locker/ Desk No.	Course & Section No.

COPY

Signature		Date	Witness/TA		Date

Note: Place fold-over back cover under copy sheet before writing

Exp. No.	Experiment/Subject		Date	
Name	Lab Partner		Locker/ Desk No.	Course & Section No.

Signature	Date	Witness/TA	Date

Exp. No.	Experiment/Subject		Date	
Name	Lab Partner		Locker/ Desk No.	Course & Section No.

Signature	Date	Witness/TA	Date

Exp. No.	Experiment/Subject		Date	
Name		Lab Partner	Locker/ Desk No.	Course & Section No.

Signature		Date	Witness/TA		Date

Exp. No.	Experiment/Subject		Date	
Name	Lab Partner		Locker/ Desk No.	Course & Section No.

Signature		Date	Witness/TA		Date

Signature		Date	Witness/TA		Date

Exp. No.	Experiment/Subject		Date	
Name	Lab Partner		Locker/ Desk No.	Course & Section No.

Signature		Date	Witness/TA		Date

Exp. No.	Experiment/Subject		Date	
Name	Lab Partner		Locker/ Desk No.	Course & Section No.

Signature		Date	Witness/TA		Date

Exp. No.	Experiment/Subject		Date	
Name	Lab Partner		Locker/ Desk No.	Course & Section No.

Signature	Date	Witness/TA	Date

Exp. No.	Experiment/Subject		Date	
Name	Lab Partner		Locker/Desk No.	Course & Section No.

Signature		Date	Witness/TA		Date

Exp. No.	Experiment/Subject		Date	
Name	Lab Partner		Locker/ Desk No.	Course & Section No.

Signature		Date	Witness/TA		Date

Exp. No.	Experiment/Subject		Date	
Name	Lab Partner		Locker/ Desk No.	Course & Section No.

Signature		Date	Witness/TA		Date

Exp. No.	Experiment/Subject		Date	
Name	Lab Partner		Locker/ Desk No.	Course & Section No.

COPY

Signature		Date	Witness/TA		Date

Exp. No.	Experiment/Subject		Date	
Name	Lab Partner		Locker/ Desk No.	Course & Section No.

Signature		Date	Witness/TA		Date

Exp. No.	Experiment/Subject		Date	
Name	Lab Partner		Locker/ Desk No.	Course & Section No.

COPY

Signature		Date	Witness/TA		Date

Exp. No.	Experiment/Subject		Date	
Name		Lab Partner	Locker/ Desk No.	Course & Section No.

Signature		Date	Witness/TA		Date

Exp. No.	Experiment/Subject		Date	
Name	Lab Partner		Locker/ Desk No.	Course & Section No.

COPY

Signature		Date	Witness/TA		Date

Exp. No.	Experiment/Subject		Date	
Name	Lab Partner		Locker/ Desk No.	Course & Section No.

Signature		Date	Witness/TA		Date

Exp. No.	Experiment/Subject		Date	
Name		Lab Partner	Locker/ Desk No.	Course & Section No.

Signature		Date	Witness/TA		Date

THE HAYDEN-McNEIL STUDENT LAB NOTEBOOK   Note: Place fold-over back cover under copy sheet before writing

Exp. No.	Experiment/Subject		Date	
Name	Lab Partner		Locker/ Desk No.	Course & Section No.

COPY

Signature	Date	Witness/TA	Date

Exp. No.	Experiment/Subject		Date	
Name	Lab Partner		Locker/ Desk No.	Course & Section No.

Signature		Date	Witness/TA		Date

Exp. No.	Experiment/Subject		Date	
Name	Lab Partner		Locker/ Desk No.	Course & Section No.

Signature		Date	Witness/TA		Date

Exp. No.	Experiment/Subject		Date	
Name		Lab Partner	Locker/ Desk No.	Course & Section No.

COPY

Signature		Date	Witness/TA		Date

THE HAYDEN-McNEIL STUDENT LAB NOTEBOOK Note: Place fold-over back cover under copy sheet before writing

Exp. No.	Experiment/Subject		Date	
Name	Lab Partner		Locker/ Desk No.	Course & Section No.

Signature		Date	Witness/TA		Date

THE HAYDEN-McNEIL STUDENT LAB NOTEBOOK

Note: Place fold-over back cover under copy sheet before writing

Exp. No.	Experiment/Subject		Date	
Name	Lab Partner		Locker/ Desk No.	Course & Section No.

Signature	Date	Witness/TA		Date

THE HAYDEN-McNEIL STUDENT LAB NOTEBOOK

Note: Place fold-over back cover under copy sheet before writing

Exp. No.	Experiment/Subject		Date	
Name	Lab Partner		Locker/ Desk No.	Course & Section No.

Signature		Date	Witness/TA		Date

THE HAYDEN-McNEIL STUDENT LAB NOTEBOOK

Note: Place fold-over back cover under copy sheet before writing

Exp. No.	Experiment/Subject		Date	
Name	Lab Partner		Locker/ Desk No.	Course & Section No.

Signature		Date	Witness/TA		Date

Exp. No.	Experiment/Subject		Date	
Name	Lab Partner		Locker/ Desk No.	Course & Section No.

Signature		Date	Witness/TA		Date

THE HAYDEN-McNEIL STUDENT LAB NOTEBOOK

Note: Place fold-over back cover under copy sheet before writing